Note to Parents

These books have been developed to introduce
young children to the concept and pleasure of
reading through a shared experience with an
adult or older brother or sister.

The books are designed to be enjoyed at three
levels of ability:
   1. Read the story to your child and discuss
what is happening in the pictures. Recognition of
words and relating them to pictures and actions is
an important part of learning to read.
   2. As your child becomes more familiar with
the story and with many of the key words, which
are reinforced through repetition, the key line
underneath each picture may be taught. This will
be the child's first experience of reading the story
for themselves.
   3. As reading ability and word recognition
progresses, your child can then graduate to the
main text. The subject matter and pattern of
words has been carefully chosen to appeal to the
young reader. The repetition in the story will help
to set words and word patterns in the young
reader's mind.

From a very early age, the young reader will
find the books rewarding, as, going through the
above stages, they will experience a feeling of
progression and achievement.

To help develop your child's interest in reading
and word recognition, there are some
suggestions for follow-up activities at the back of
the book.

Barry Hill

Dan's Day Out

written by Barry Hill
illustrated by Heather Clarke

Copyright © 1991 by World International Publishing Ltd.
All rights reserved.
Published in Great Britain by World International Publishing Ltd.,
An Egmont Company, Egmont House, P.O.Box 111,
Great Ducie Street, Manchester M60 3BL.
Printed in Germany. ISBN 0 7498 0130 1

A CIP catalogue record for this book is available from the British Library

It was a warm, summer's day at Blossom Farm. Dan had been playing in the farmyard all morning. He was enjoying the warm sunshine on his back.

Most of the animals were out in the fields. I think I would like to play in the fields now, thought Dan at last. **Dan wanted to be with his friends**.

So he trotted past the stable. He trotted past the pig sty. He trotted past the hen house. He trotted past the cow shed. And he came to a gate that led into a field of green grass.

**Dan wanted to be with
his friends.**

Dan scrambled under the gate into the field, where the foal was grazing happily. "What are you doing?" Dan asked.

The foal whinnied. "I'm enjoying all this grass."

"It doesn't sound very exciting to me," said Dan.

"What do you want to do?" asked the foal.

Dan thought for a minute. "I know," he said. "I'll race you across the field."

So **Dan and the foal had a race.** They raced across the field until they reached the other side. Dan just won!

Dan and the foal had a race.

"That was great," said Dan when they reached the other side of the field. "I only just won."

"I'll race you back," said the foal.

But **Dan saw another field** of green grass on the other side of the hedge. "I don't want to go back just yet," said Dan. "I think I'll go into the next field and see who's in there."

"Very well," said the foal. "But don't go too far. You may get lost."

"I won't get lost," said Dan.

Dan saw another field.

Dan scrambled through a gap in the hedge
and into the next field, where a calf was
grazing happily. "I'll race you across the
field," Dan called.

So **Dan and the calf had a race.**
They raced across the field until they
reached the other side. And Dan just won
again!

Dan was enjoying himself. "I think I'll go into
the next field and see who's in there,"
he said.

"Very well," said the calf. "But don't go
too far. You may get lost."

"I won't get lost," said Dan.

Dan and the calf had a race.

Dan scrambled through a gap in the hedge and into the next field, where a lamb was grazing happily. "I'll race you across the field," Dan called.

So **Dan and the lamb had a race.**
They raced across the field until they reached the other side. And Dan just won again!

Dan was enjoying himself more than ever. "I think I'll go into the next field and see who's in there," he said.

"Very well," said the lamb. "But don't go too far. You may get lost."

"I won't get lost," said Dan.

Dan and the lamb had a race.

Dan scrambled through a gap in the hedge and ... "Aarrgh!" He stepped back in surprise.

There wasn't a field of green grass. There were no friends to play with. **Dan was beside a busy road.** A very busy road, with cars and vans racing past.

Dan was frightened. He had spent most of his days in the quiet farmyard. He had never seen a busy road before. I don't like this, thought Dan, as another car raced by. I don't like this at all. I think it's time I went home.

Dan was beside a busy road.

Dan scrambled back through the gap in the hedge. Once again he was in a field of green grass. He looked round for his friend, the lamb. I'll race him back across the field, he thought.

But Dan couldn't see the lamb. He looked this way and that, but all he could see was green grass.

Dan suddenly felt frightened again. I know I came across this field, he thought.
But which way did I come? Which is the way back home?

He sat down. The one thing that the foal and the calf and the lamb had warned him about had happened. **Dan was lost.**

Dan was lost.

What am I going to do? wondered Dan.
I could be out here all night. Just then,
he heard a rustle in a nearby tree. It was his
friend, the crow. "You don't look very happy,"
cawed the crow.

"I'm not," said Dan. "I can't find my
way home."

"It's lucky I came along then," cawed the
crow. **I can show you the way home.**
But you must promise me one thing.
You must promise that you will never stray
away from home again."

"I promise. I promise," said Dan.

"I can show you the way home."

The crow flew into the air. "I can see the farmhouse from here," it cawed. "Follow me, and I'll soon have you home."

Dan followed the crow as it flew off across the field.

Soon they came to a hedge. Dan scrambled through a gap into the next field. The crow flew on.

Soon they came to another hedge. Dan scrambled through a gap into the next field. Still the crow flew on.

At last, they came to a gate. On the other side of the gate was Dan's farmyard.

Dan followed the crow.

"Thank you. Thank you," Dan said. He was so pleased to be home. The tired puppy was back in the farmyard safe and sound. **Dan was home again!**

Dan's friends were all there when he got back.

"I may not be able to run as fast as you," the foal whinnied. "But I don't get lost."

"I may not be able to run as fast as you," the calf mooed. "But I don't get lost."

"I may not be able to run as fast as you," the lamb baaed. "But I don't get lost."

And you can be sure that from that day on, Dan never strayed far enough away from his home to get lost, either!

Dan was home again!

These are the key lines from the story in this book, together with representations of the pictures.

Read each line, matching it up with the picture. Then look at the picture and encourage your child to recall the key line. Repeat the line word by word to encourage recognition.

When this has been achieved, as a game you might ask your child how much he or she can recall about the story.

Dan wanted to be with his friends.

Dan and the foal had a race.

Dan saw another field.

Dan and the calf had a race.

Dan and the lamb had a race.

Dan was beside a busy road.

Dan was lost.

"I can show you the way home."

Dan followed the crow.

Dan was home again!

FOLLOW-UP ACTIVITIES
Word and sound recognition: Identify words from the story that have a similarity, ie, sound the same, have the same-sounding endings. Can the young reader think of any other words not in the story that have the same ending?

Observation: Encourage the child to translate what he or she sees into words – initially just the object word, then add adjectives, eg, a field, a green field.

Storytelling: Encourage the child to make up his or her own stories about the characters in the book, or tell of an experience, real or imaginary, involving a puppy, hen, cow, pig, sheep, horse, etc.

Recall: Encourage the child to recite nursery rhymes about the animals and birds mentioned in the story.